The Official Annual 2014

Contents

BFF

Do you know the five friends from Heartlake City? Can you match the correct symbol, description and picture for each girl below?

Mia – she's very fond of nature and loves taking care of animals.

Emma – she has a really artistic soul. The simplest things inspire her to create brilliant projects.

Stephanie – she just loves making plans and lists! She enjoys organizing parties and writing books.

Andrea – she's destined to be a star. First, she needs to decide what she loves best – singing or dancing?!

Olivia – she's a total science expert and great at photography and DIY.

Join us!

Imagine you've joined the Heartlake City bunch.
What nicknames would you give your new friends?
Write them in the spaces above.

Olivia's Surprise

Olivia

Andrea

Emma

Stephanie

Mia

Olivia is preparing a surprise for her friends, but oops! All her photos have fallen out of the album! Can you count how many times each girl appears in the photos and write the number in the circles?

In Close-up

Look at Olivia's picture of the girls having a crazy pillow fight. Can you tell which puzzle piece is not part of the photo?

Origami Butterfly

Emma knows everything about crafts and can make great things out of paper. Follow her tips to make a colourful origami butterfly.

You will need a 10 x 10 cm square piece of paper.

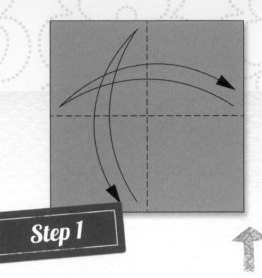

Step 1

Fold the sheet in half along the dotted lines, then unfold it. Fold it in half the other way and unfold again. The creases will create the shape of a cross.

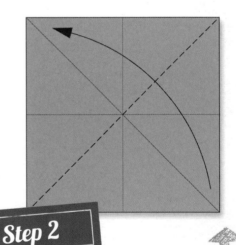

Step 2

Now fold it in half diagonally both ways. When you finish, the creases will create the shape of a star.

Step 3

Fold the sheet in half to make a rectangle. Now fold the right and left edge inside. You should get a triangle.

Step 4

Fold the left and right flap up along the dotted lines. Remember to leave the flaps on the underside unfolded.

Step 5

Turn the shape over and fold the bottom part up, as shown in the picture.

Step 6

Turn the shape over again. Fold the two flaps down. Then, fold the edge of each towards the inside, so that the folded line is hidden inside.

Step 7

Turn the shape over once again. Fold the top flap down along the lines. Then fold it in half to shape the butterfly's head.

Step 8

Fold the model in half. Now your butterfly is ready! Try making more colourful origami butterflies and use them to decorate your room. Or you can give them to your best friends as gifts.

Olivia's room is decorated with photos of her friends and pets. Draw a picture of your best friend or pet here.
Try adding a funky doodle frame, too!

Olivia's room

Show Time

Have you ever dreamt of putting on a show for your friends? All you need to do is to follow Andrea's tips!

Tip 1 Before you start practising for your show, you need to decide whether you want to do a theatre play, dance show, magic tricks or a music recital. Once you've made up your mind, you can get started!

Tip 2 First you need to choose the right place to perform, with enough room for a stage and places for people to sit. Mark out your stage on the floor and have chairs and soft cushions so your audience can sit down.

Tip 3 Get together everything you need for your performance, including what you want to wear, so you're not rushing around at the last minute.

Tip 4 It's a good idea to rehearse your show beforehand. The more you practise, the better impression you will make on your friends.

Pixie ✸

When your friends are ready for your show, you can sing them this song. Remember to put these verses in the correct order.

Our song

○ And suddenly everything changed
My biggest dream came true.
I met you on my way
I no longer felt so blue.

○ Since then it's always you and me!
No matter what the weather,
We'll play, laugh and have fun
In harmony forever.

○ I still remember the gloomy days
When I felt so alone
And not even a single ring
Was heard on my phone.

Unbelievable!

Olivia knows more than anyone how fascinating science can be. Recently she has been studying optical illusions! Help her answer these questions.

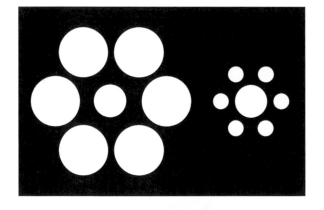

1. Colour the flowers. Which one has the biggest centre?

2. Trace the grey lines. How many shelves can you see?

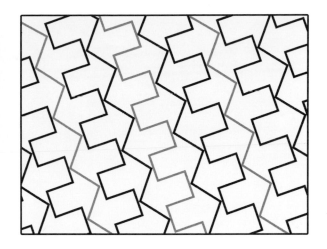

3. Colour the grey boxes. Are the lines straight?

4. Then, try to figure out which direction the arrows go in.

5. Trace the grey lines with a red felt-tip pen. Can you see which black line is longer and which is shorter?

6. Study the circles for a while. Which one is swirling faster?

How fast can you spot the things that don't belong to each friend? Stephanie knows her friends inside-out, so it only takes her a minute!

What a Blunder!

Even the most serious situation can be funny! Look at these embarrassing moments and give them a score of 1 to 5, with '1' being the funniest. You could also try making a list of your own embarrassing moments with your friends.

Emma designed a fancy new swimsuit for the mayor to wear at the opening of a new swimming pool in Heartlake City. Unfortunately, the outfit was a bit too original!

Andrea baked cookies in the café for her friends and attached little notes to them saying how much she liked the girls, but she accidently served them to a group of boys instead! Oops!

Olivia made the smallest microphone in the world especially for Andrea. Unfortunately it was so small, the girls are still trying to find where it is!

Mia was in such a hurry to play football with her friends that she forgot to change her pretty pink T-shirt for a sporty top.

Stephanie forgot to hide the cake she made for Mia's birthday and her little doggy found it before she did!

Bling My Dress!

Andrea is going to sing at the Creativity Festival and needs an amazing dress. Help her out by finishing the pretty pattern below!

Café Rush

Sometimes there is such a rush in the café where Andrea works that it's very hard to keep up with everything that's going on. Look at the pictures and try to find 10 differences.

Journey to the Future

The five friends are talking about their dreams. Match the girls with what they would like to be when they're older. Fill in what you would like to do, too.

vet

scientist

I'd like to be a ...

journalist

singer

fashion designer

Special Gift

Olivia's birthday is in a couple of days and her friends want to give her something special.
Read the girls' chat and choose the best gift below.

Colourful Dizziness

Every girl has a favourite colour! Can you colour in their t-shirts, keeping in mind that Olivia can't resist aqua blue, Mia loves green, Emma likes purple, Andrea is fond of everything yellow and Stephanie adores hot pink.

Find out what your favourite colour says about you!

Yellow – this colour is for people who are joyful and spontaneous. If this is your perfect match it means your friends think you are a likeable and trustworthy person.

Green – this colour means openness, sincerity and kindness. If you choose green you are surely a creative person – your head is full of ideas and you like it when there are lots of things going on around you.

Blue – this colour is for dreamers. If this is your favourite, then you have an artist's soul. Your friends admire your ability to create beautiful things.

Red – if this is your favourite colour it means you are energetic, brave and self-confident. You know exactly what you want and you usually achieve your goals.

Pink – symbolizes honesty, sensitivity and protectiveness. If you choose pink it means that you're a hopeless romantic, dreaming of being swept off your feet!

Purple – this colour is for people who are generous and emotional but also indecisive. They are very intuitive, but their complex natures mean they have lots of paths to follow, and they're never sure which one to take.

Mia's Lesson

Ecology is very important for Mia so she has decided to prepare a school project about it. Read the sentences below and decide which option in each pair is the most friendly to the environment.

travelling by bicycle * travelling by plane

long bath * short shower

plastic bag * fabric bag

juicy apple * chocolate bar

juice in a glass bottle * juice in a plastic bottle

fabric towel * paper towel

Zobo the Hairdresser

Eco Necklace

Mia's school project has inspired Emma to create her own jewellery collection. Follow her example and design your own eco necklace!

Flying High

Stephanie is flying high above Heartlake City in her hydroplane. Take a look at the beautiful view and try to find the stables, Heartlake Harbour and the campsite.

Ideal Holiday

Choose one word from each group that you like the most.
Then count up how many of each symbol you've chosen.
The one you've picked the most is your ideal holiday!

- water
- air
- ground

- dolphin
- squirrel
- eagle

- ground floor
- cellar
- attic

- blue
- green
- yellow

What symbol did you get the most?

Hedgehog – You're always looking for an adventure! Your perfect unforgettable holiday would be camping in the Whispering Woods!

Bird – You find nothing more enjoyable than wandering along the trails in the Clearspring Mountains. You'd love to reach the highest peak and enjoy the view!

Crab – All you need is sun, sea and sand! Your ideal place for a holiday is the beautiful Ambersands Beach.

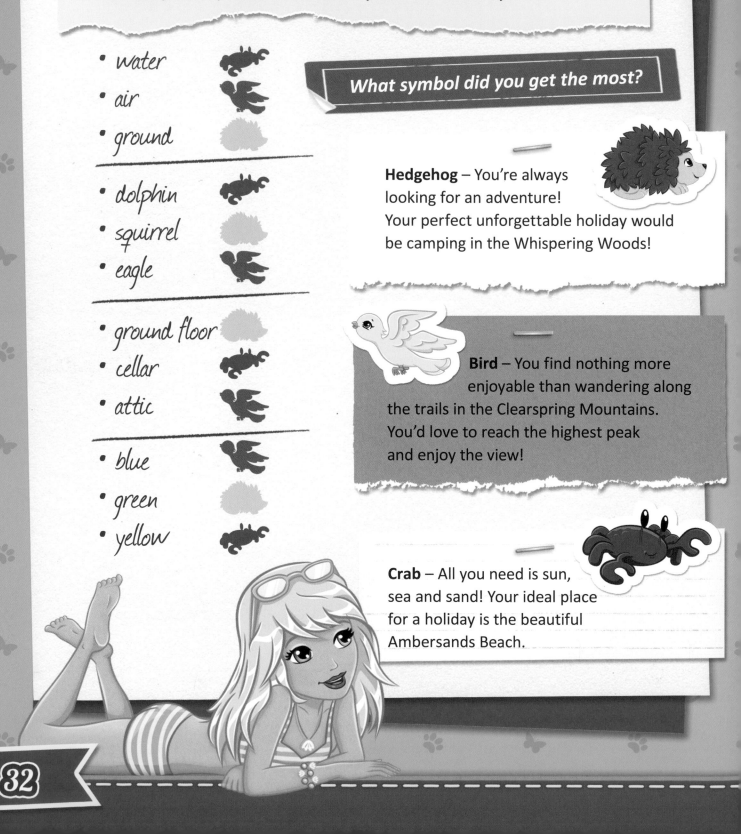

CARTE POSTALE
POST CARD - BRIEFKAART

ADDRESS:

Design a holiday postcard for your best friend.
When you've finished reading this book you can
cut it out, stick the pieces together and send it.
Don't forget the stamp!

Magic Cards

Mia loves learning new magic tricks – especially with cards! Look at the card sequences below. Can you figure out which of the four cards belong in the gaps?

Mia's Sudoku

Complete this picture sudoku of the girls' pets by writing the correct letter in the spaces. No picture should be repeated in each row, column or 4x4 square.

A

B

C

D

Concert Trip

The girls are running late for Andrea's concert! Lead them through the maze as quickly as you can, avoiding all the obstacles.

There are many beautiful horses at the Heartlake Stables. These simple steps show how to draw one of them.

1

2

3

4

5

6

Rainbow Party

There's nothing better than throwing a party for friends – and it's even more fun if there's a theme! Read Stephanie's top tips for planning an awesome party.

★ Before you start the preparations, you should think about a theme for your event. How about a rainbow party?

★ Now it's time for the invitations. You will need a drawing pad, felt-tip pens, colourful paper, scissors and glue. Make sure you let your guests know about the party theme. You can also ask them to dress up! If you choose a rainbow theme, you could ask everyone to wear their favourite colour!

★ Don't forget about rainbow decorations: prepare colourful cups, napkins, garlands and streamers.

★ Your party won't be a success without good food. How about baking rainbow muffins? Or maybe you could prepare a colourful ice-cream dessert or a delicious salad made out of colourful fruits?

★ You should also organize some nice music and fun games to keep your guests entertained. Follow my advice and you'll be the party-planning queen!

Good food is one of the most important things at any party.
Make this cake look scrumptious by colouring it in!

My Cake

Unusual Experiment

Olivia and Emma like working together to make things scientific and creative! Try making this solar clock with one of your friends!

You will need:
- a round paper plate
- a pencil
- a drinking straw
- modelling clay
- crayons, felt-tip pens and other accessories that you can use for decoration
- a pair of scissors

Step 1a

Step 1b

Turn the plate upside down and make a small hole in the middle. Put the drinking straw in it so that almost all of the straw sticks ut of the plate. To make the straw stable, secure it with modelling clay underneath. Then, draw 12 short lines equally spaced apart.

Step 2

Now, place your solar clock in a very sunny place. When the time strikes the top of the hour, e.g. 1 o'clock, check where the shadow of the straw falls. Move the plate so that the shadow falls exactly on a line and mark it with the correct hour.

Ready!

After marking the first hour, complete your clock plate by filling in the other numbers. You can check the lines are in the right place when the clock strikes every hour. You can also decorate your plate to make it special!

The five friends from Heartlake City love taking group photos. Each time, a different girl plays photographer so that nobody feels left out. Take a look at the photos and guess whose turn it is.

② ⑥

⑧

⑦

⑨

Mirror, Mirror

Wow! Emma was asked to give a makeover to a friend from school. The result was totally astonishing! Try to match the reflection below with the picture on the right.

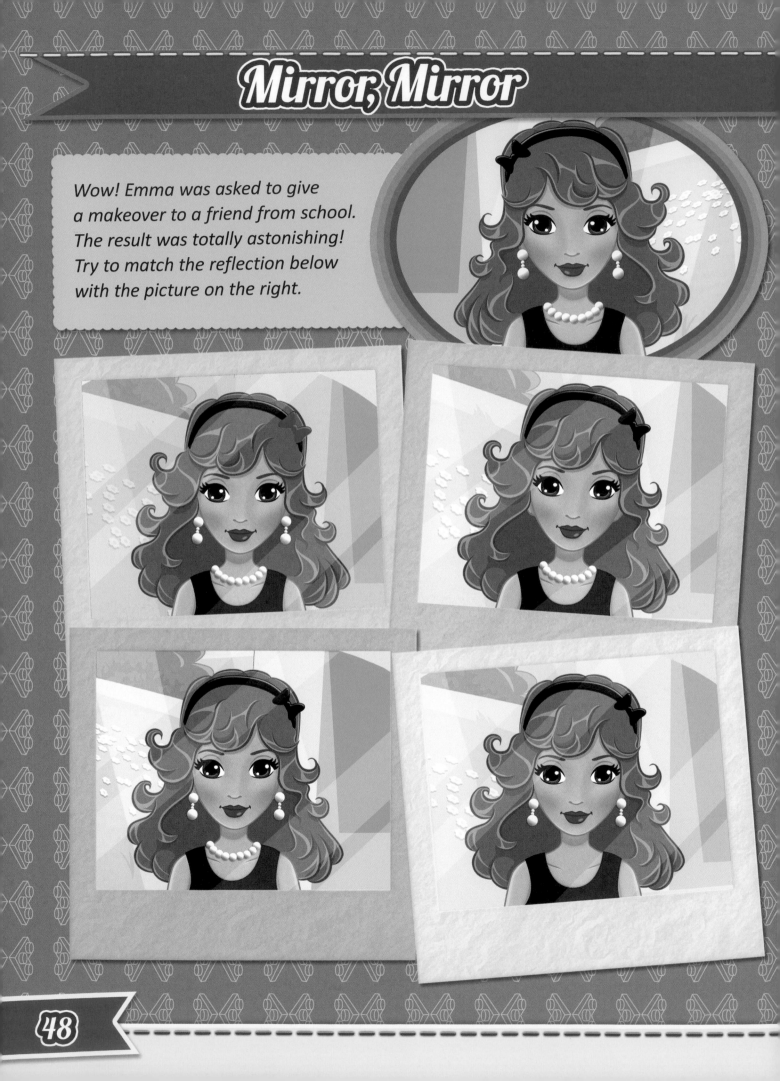

What do you think is going on in the picture below? Write the note Andrea is reading, and her response!

Best Friends

Tick the most important qualities you think a best friend should have!

An ideal friend should:

- be nice
- know how to keep secrets
- wear stylish clothes
- be pretty
- like similar things
- get good grades at school
- be popular
- listen to my favourite music
- be sincere
- laugh at the same jokes

A good friend is a treasure. The girls have lots of tips for making new best friends!

A) Get out and mingle! The more you meet people, the more friends you'll make!

B) Think of people who have similar interests. If you like the same things, there is a great chance that you will become friends.

C) Don't forget to smile. A happy face is key to making new friends.

D) Friendship is about the little details. Try to remember your friend's birthday and all the things that are important to her.

E) And most of all, be yourself! People want to make friends with you – not the person you pretend to be.

Caricature

Real friends can laugh at themselves!
Try drawing a caricature of a friend,
and ask her to do one of you!

Emma's top tips!

Start with the head: it should be much bigger than the rest of the body. You could just draw your friend's face if you prefer.

Now for the details: pay attention to the most characteristic features of the person you're drawing, like eyes, nose or lips. Does your friend have freckles? Or maybe she makes funny faces or wears an original hairdo? Make sure to exaggerate your friend's most distinctive features!

Most importantly!

Always remember: caricatures are meant to be funny, not mean! Good friends don't upset each other, so keep it cute.

This is ....

Puzzle Game

The girls love lazing and swimming at the Heartlake City Pool. Can you arrange the puzzle pieces below to see what they're doing?

Having a group of five friends is great! Try writing seven words about friendship starting with each of the letters in 'FRIENDS'.

✓ Friends forever ♡
u
n

F ....

R ....

I ....

E ....

N ....

D ....

S ....

Friendship bracelet

Answers

BFF p. 4

♡		Olivia
♪		Andrea
❀		Emma
☆		Stephanie
🐾		Mia

Olivia's Surprise p. 6

Olivia — 2

Andrea — 3

Emma — 6

Stephanie — 5

Mia — 5

In Close-up p. 7

Show Time p. 13

2, 3, 1

Unbelievable! p. 14

1. Both centres are the same
2. There are two shelves
3. All lines are straight
4. The arrows go in both directions
5. Both lines are the same length
6. None. The circles are swirling at the same speed

Mismatch! p. 18

Café Rush p. 21

Journey to the Future p. 22

scientist

vet

I'd like to be a ...

singer

fashion designer

journalist

Special Gift p. 23

Mia's Lesson p. 26

travelling by bicycle * travelling by plane

long bath * short shower

plastic bag * fabric bag

juicy apple * chocolate bar

juice in a glass bottle * juice in a plastic bottle

fabric towel * paper towel

Bird's-eye View p. 30

Magic Cards p. 34

Mia's Sudoku p. 35

Answers

Concert Trip p. 36

Who's the Photographer? p. 46
1. Olivia
2. Olivia
3. Olivia
4. Stephanie
5. Mia
6. Stephanie
7. Mia
8. Andrea
9. Mia

Mirror, Mirror p. 48

Puzzle Game p. 54

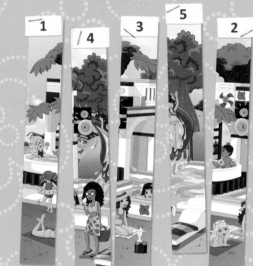

Olivia ♡

Emma ❀

Mia 🦋

Stephanie ✺

Andrea ♫